What Else Can I Play
Piano
Grade One

Good for Xmas stuff

All Through The Night		12
Edelweiss		16
✓ A Groovy Kind Of Love		3
✓ Heigh-Ho		10
✓ The Holly And The Ivy		7
I Vow To Thee, My Country		24
Lavender's Blue		6
✓ Little Donkey		4
Lullaby Waltz		13
Morning		14
Neighbours		30
✓ Rudolph The Red-Nosed Reindeer		8
Smile		18
Some Day My Prince Will Come		26
The Sun Has Got His Hat On		20
The Teddy Bears' Picnic		28
When You Wish Upon A Star		22
You'll Never Walk Alone		19

Series Editor: Mark Mumford

Music arranged and processed by
Barnes Music Engraving Ltd
East Sussex TN22 4HA, England

Published 1995

Introduction

In this *What Else Can I Play?* collection you'll find eighteen popular tunes that are both challenging and entertaining.

The pieces have been carefully selected and arranged to create ideal supplementary material for young pianists who are either working towards or have recently taken a Grade One piano examination.

Technical demands increase progressively, gradually introducing new concepts that reflect the requirements of the major examination boards. Each piece offers suggestions and guidelines to fingering, dynamics and tempo, together with technical tips and performance notes.

Pupils will experience a wide variety of music, ranging from folk and classical through to showtunes and popular songs, leading to a greater awareness of musical styles.

Whether it's for light relief from examination preparation, or to reinforce the understanding of new concepts, this collection will enthuse and encourage all young piano players.

A groovy kind of love

Words and Music by Toni Wine and Carole Bayer-Sager

This song was written in the 1960s when the word 'groovy', meaning exciting or fashionable, was often used. The song was also a big hit for Phil Collins in the 1980s.

Watch your fingering in this piece as there are some tricky changes of hand position, especially in the left hand. You will also notice that the song begins on the third beat of the bar instead of the first beat. This often happens in all styles of music and is known as an *anacrusis*.

Little donkey

Words and Music by Eric Boswell

This nativity song, with its simple melody, has continued to be a favourite since its composition in 1959.

Have a look at the crotchets in the left hand of this piece. This style of accompaniment writing, which is made up of broken chords, is known as *Alberti Bass*. As with all accompaniment lines, don't allow it to overpower the melody in the right hand.

5

Lavender's blue

Traditional

Gentle Minuet ($\quartnote$ = 116)

You may remember this nursery rhyme from when you were younger. It dates from around 1672 but was originally called *Diddle-diddle* or *The Kind Country Lovers*.

This piece needs a light staccato touch, so try keeping your wrists raised towards the fingerboard. Have a go at practising the left hand separately, at first. Try to get the join between the first and second beats as smooth and light as you can.

The holly and the ivy

Traditional

The Holly And The Ivy is a traditional Gloucestershire folk-carol. The writer and exact date of the piece remain unknown.

Look carefully at the crescendo and diminuendo marks ('hairpins') in this piece. Notice how the rise and fall of the melody is mirrored by the dynamics.

Rudolph the red-nosed reindeer

Words and Music by Johnny Marks

This bouncy song is a Christmas favourite. Poor Rudolph is picked on by the other reindeer because of his bright red nose. However, when Santa Claus asks Rudolph to guide his sleigh through a foggy Christmas Eve, he soon becomes the most popular reindeer of all. Can you name the other reindeer?

Don't be put off by the rhythmic syncopation in this melody. Dividing two beats into three this way occurs quite often in showtunes and other popular music. Try clapping the rhythm before you play. Don't forget to continue the staccato in the left hand from bar 3 and be prepared for the *D.C. al Fine* at bar 24.

Heigh-ho

Words by Larry Morey, Music by Frank E. Churchill

This is perhaps the most famous song from the film *Snow White And The Seven Dwarfs* (1937), Walt Disney's first full-length animated film. The film took three years to make and was a huge success.

Notice that, like a lot of popular music, this piece has an introduction before the well-known chorus which starts at bar 17. Keep the repeated staccato notes light. You'll find them easier to play if you relax your wrist.

All through the night

Welsh Traditional

All Through The Night is the English name by which the Welsh folk-song *Ar Hyd y Nos* is known.

Your hands are very close together in this piece. In the second bar, for example, the right hand takes over a note from the left hand. When this happens don't be tempted to shorten the note values.

Lullaby waltz

Johannes Brahms

Johannes Brahms (1833–1897) was a German pianist and composer who was greatly influenced by German folk music and Hungarian violin music. Some of his earliest playing engagements were in dockside taverns.

A lullaby is a cradle song, sung to soothe a young child to sleep. Think about this as you are playing. Using the pads of your fingers instead of the tips will help you produce a gentler and softer tone. Keep your wrists relaxed especially in the left hand.

Morning

Edvard Grieg

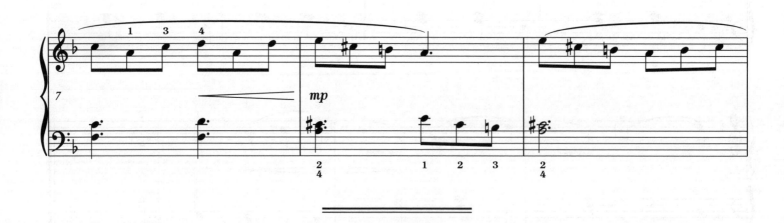

Morning is the first movement of a suite of pieces by the Norwegian composer Edvard Grieg (1843–1907). The suite was written as incidental music to Ibsen's play *Peer Gynt* and also contains the famous *In The Hall Of The Mountain King*.

Pay careful attention to the phrasing in this piece. Keep the quavers even and controlled and don't rush the semiquavers – they are not as fast as they look! Notice how the dynamics gradually build up through the piece until the loudest point at bar 21.

Edelweiss

Words by Oscar Hammerstein II, Music by Richard Rodgers

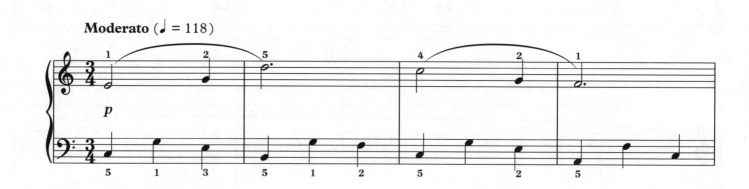

The edelweiss is the national flower of Switzerland. The song *Edelweiss* is sung by Maria in the celebrated musical *The Sound Of Music*. The partnership of the writers Rodgers and Hammerstein was responsible for some of the most famous musicals ever staged, including *South Pacific*, *The King And I*, *Carousel* and *Oklahoma!*

The melody, which includes some very short phrases, is quite 'singable'. Try to play it as you would imagine it being sung to bring out the musical 'sentences'. Watch out for the crescendo and diminuendo in the middle section – but don't overdo it!

Smile

Words by John Turner and Geoffrey Parsons, Music by Charles Chaplin

The composer of this music is better known as Charlie rather than Charles. Charlie Chaplin is famous as an actor in silent films but, as is often forgotten, was also a director and accomplished composer.

The melody of this song is largely made up of scale passages, so pay careful attention to your fingering. Despite the title, this is not a happy tune – it's rather a reflective melody. Try to capture the thoughtful mood.

You'll never walk alone

Words by Oscar Hammerstein II, Music by Richard Rodgers

You'll Never Walk Alone is the finale from the 1945 musical *Carousel*. The show was a huge hit, making eight hundred and ninety performances in its first run.

The slow pace of this piece is almost hymn-like. Try to produce a very firm legato tone ensuring note values are held for their full length. Be sure to capture the emotional ending by noting the long and gradual crescendo that starts in bar 12.

The sun has got his hat on

Words and Music by Ralph Butler and Noel Gay

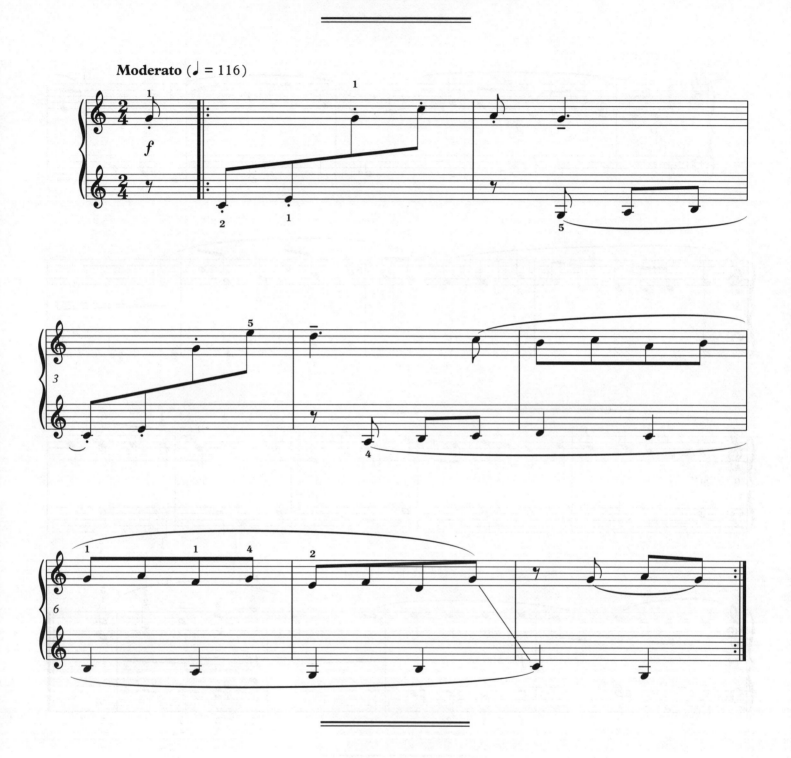

This 1930s hit was very popular during the Second World War and received a surprise hit revival in the 1960s from a group called *The Temperance Seven*.

The melody in this piece is divided between both hands, with the left hand also using the treble clef. Try to make a marked contrast between staccato notes and the legato passages.

When you wish upon a star

Words by Ned Washington, Music by Leigh Harline

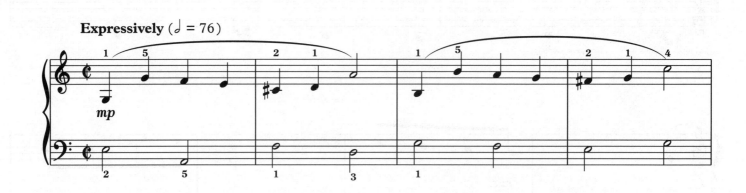

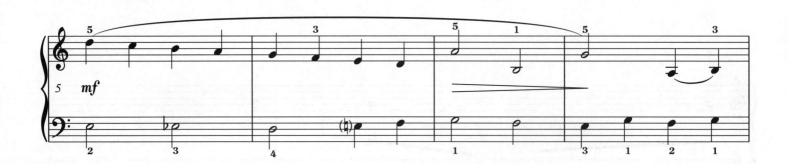

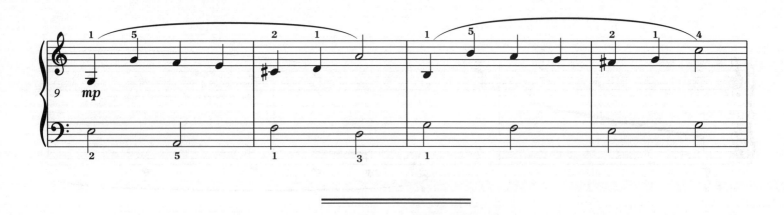

When You Wish Upon A Star is taken from Walt Disney's 1940 animated film, *Pinocchio*, for which it won an Academy Award for Original Song.

The melody in this piece tends to leap around so pay careful attention to your fingering, especially when crossing over your thumb, as in bar 2. This will help the melody flow smoothly. Beware of the accidentals in the middle section.

I vow to thee, my country

Words by Cecil Spring-Rice, Music by Gustav Holst

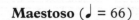

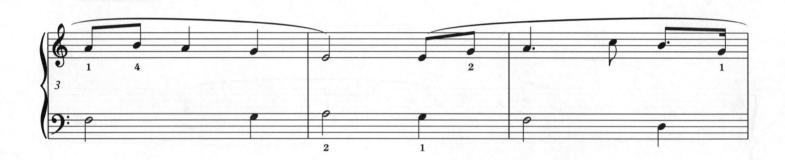

This patriotic melody originates from Gustav Holst's gigantic suite for orchestra, *The Planets*. It appears in the fourth movement, which is named after the planet *Jupiter*. Later Holst re-arranged the tune for choir and orchestra, using Cecil Spring-Rice's words. It has been a popular hymn ever since.

Try to bring out the dignified mood of this piece. *Maestoso* means majestically, so aim for a steady and even beat with carefully marked phrases. Note the dynamics too, especially at the end of the final phrase.

Some day my prince will come

Words by Larry Morey, Music by Frank E. Churchill

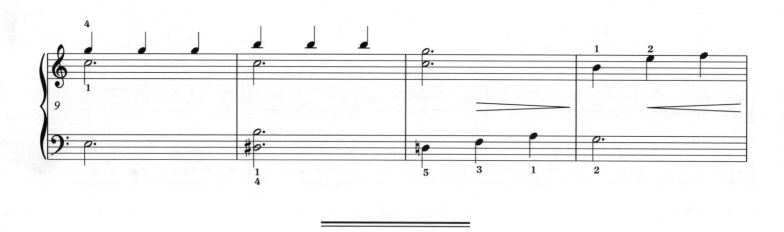

This tune is from the film animation *Snow White And The Seven Dwarfs* (1937). It is a wistful ballad sung by Snow White (whose cartoon form was modelled on the wife of one of the animators).

The melody in the right hand really must 'sing'. This is a playing quality which is not easily summarised, but, for any instrumental music, to evoke a singing style is known as *cantabile*. Look ahead for accidentals in the left hand part.

The teddy bears' picnic

Words by Jimmy Kennedy, Music by John Bratton

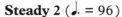

Steady 2 (♩. = 96)

This famous children's song was written in 1907. However, it was made most popular by Henry Hall and his orchestra in the 1930s. Hall was an accomplished bandleader who directed the BBC Dance Orchestra.

Make the most of the diminuendo at the beginning of this piece to create a really effective introduction. The melodic phrases rise in the first half of this piece, so take care with the changes of hand position.

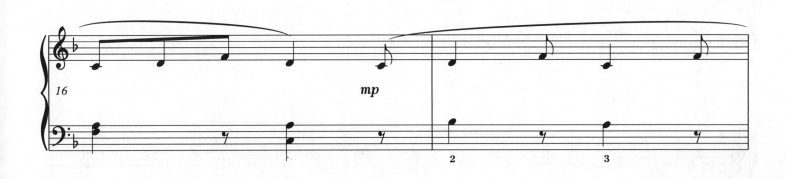

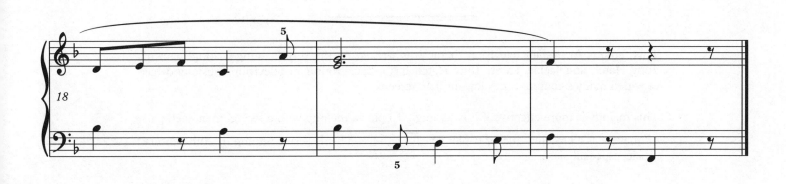

Neighbours

Words and Music by Tony Hatch and Jackie Trent

This famous Australian television theme was written by the prolific song-writing team of Tony Hatch and Jackie Trent. Tony Hatch has a background in television music and has provided many signature tunes for our T.V. screens.

This melody is more effective if it is 'swung'. To play a melody with a swing, treat each pair of quavers as a crotchet-quaver triplet i.e. ♪♪ = ♩♪. This is very common in 20th century music, especially jazz.